WALK ON THE WATER

ACCOMPANIMENT

Words and Music

by

JULIE HOWARD

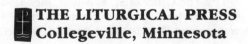
THE LITURGICAL PRESS
Collegeville, Minnesota

To
THE CRAYONS
Sts. Peter, Paul, and Michael School
St. Cloud, Minnesota

ACKNOWLEDGMENTS

Thank you to Mary Hughes for her listening ear and loving heart; to Chris Reicher for ready, steady input along the way; to the Crayons for their wonderful voices and spirit; to the Crayons' parents for their faith in me and their constant support; to Peter Dwyer for listening, advising, supporting; to Sister Christian Morris, O.S.B., for helping me to see my path; to the Franciscan Sisters at Clare's Well, Aggie and Carol, for opening my eyes to the Spirit; to my principal, Mike Mullin, for believing in me; to my friends Iris and Marly for encouraging me to continue; to Jeff Velline for caring more about music than money; to Dave Falzone for great arrangements; and to my husband Jerry for his wise counsel and love.

Julie Howard

Printed in the United States of America.

ISBN 0-8146-2012-4

CONTENTS

If You Love Me 5

Walk on the Water 8

God Is the Gas in My Go-Cart 13

Hold My Hand *(For Jacob Wetterling)* 18

Glory in the Light 20

The Zebedee Rap 24

I'm Alive with Jesus 25

Anawim Know 30

Gotta Do 33

We Goof But God Loves Us 46

Don't Look for Jesus in the Sky 51

Knock 57

God Is Like the Dawn 60

If You Love Me

(See Genesis 28:10-15)

Words and music by Julie Howard
Accompaniment by David Falzone

(Based on the traditional children's song "Jesus Loves Me")

YES   JE - SUS   LOVES ME.   YES   JE - SUS   LOVES ME.

YES   JE - SUS   LOVES ME.   MY   DREAMS ALL TELL ME   SO.

Walk on the Water

(See Matthew 14:23-33)

Words and music by Julie Howard
Accompaniment by David Falzone

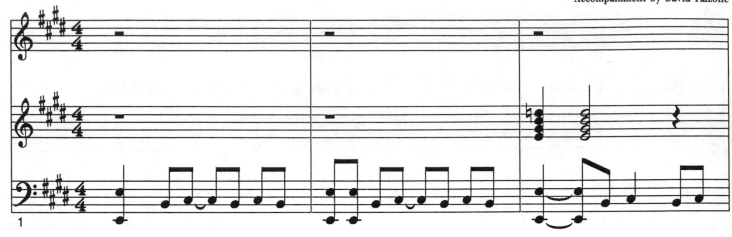

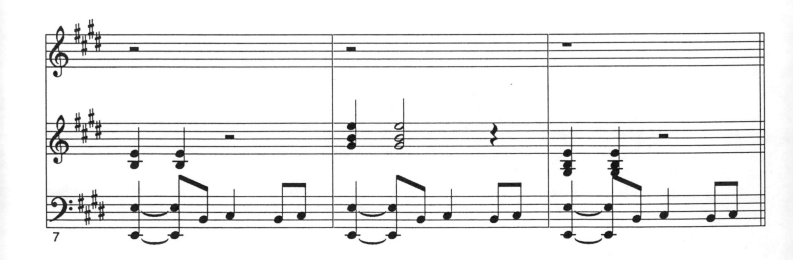

land.   Get off   the safe, dry   land.

God Is the Gas in My Go-Cart

(See Acts 2:1-4)

Words and music by Julie Howard
Accompaniment by Jeff Velline and David Falzone

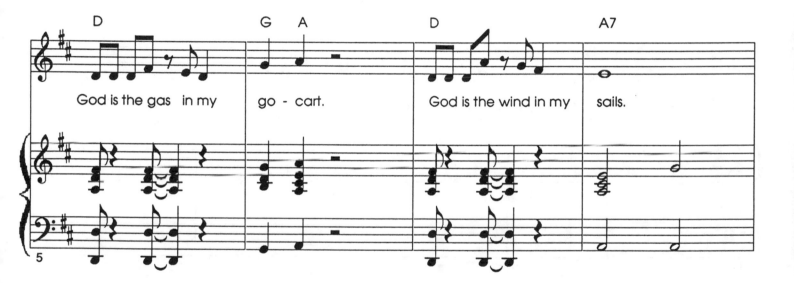

God is the gas in my go - cart. God is the wind in my sails.

God is the fire in my chuga-chug en - gine, filled up with God I can't fail.

14

God is the fire in my chuga-chug en - gine filled up with God I can't fail!

God is the rev in my Che - vy. God is the putt in my boat.

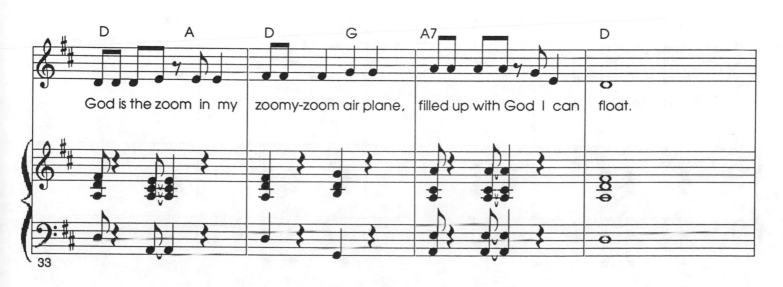

God is the zoom in my zoomy-zoom air plane, filled up with God I can float.

God is the fire in my chuga-chug en - gine, filled up with God I can't fail!

Hold My Hand
(For Jacob Wetterling)

(See Psalm 46:1-3, 7)

Words and music by Julie Howard
Accompaniment by David Falzone

Hold my hand and I will lead you; trust in me to be your guide.

Though you go through the ra - ging water, I will be at your side.

Glory in the Light

(See Jeremiah 9:22-23)

Words and music by Julie Howard
Accompaniment by David Falzone

Let not the wise glory in their wis-dom; let not the migh-ty glory in their might. Let not the rich glory in their rich-es;

22

The Zebedee Rap

(See John 21:1-14)

Words by Julie Howard

On the shore of Tiberias
the fishermen gathered again—
Peter, Nathaniel, Zebedee's sons,
and Thomas (he's called "the Twin").

Peter, the leader, jumped in the boat and said,
"I'm gonna drop the net."
"We're coming too. That's what we do,
and we hope a lotta fish we get!"
said Zebedee's sons.

"That sounds like fun!" said Thomas.
"Got room for Nate and me?"
*So Peter, Nathaniel, Zebedee's sons,
and Thomas sailed out to sea.* (Repeat)

They fished all night in the pale moonlight,
got nothing but an empty net.
They were hungry, tired, and disappointed,
but they didn't throw the towel in yet.

They tried and cried and cried and tried,
but no matter what the men would do,
those fish would not cooperate.
Oh, it really had them in a stew.
And they were getting hungry too.

When daybreak came, bad luck remained,
so they pulled the net into the boat.
*Peter, Nathaniel, Zebedee's sons,
and Thomas were losing hope.* (Repeat)

When up on the land they thought they heard
a man yell, "Children, how does it go?
Have you caught your breakfast yet?"
And the fishermen answered, "NO!"

"Drop your net on the starboard side
and you will get your wish."
They dropped it down and pulled it up—
it was loaded with a pile of fish.

"He is the Lord!" cried Zebedee's sons.
The others cried the same thing too.
"He's the Lord! He came around when we were down
and he indicated what to do."

Peter, the leader, jumped in the water,
started heading for the land.
The fishermen followed him in their tiny boat.
They were singing and a-clapping their hands.

"Come here and eat," said the man on the dry land.
"Come and have some fish and bread.
My fire is hot and you are not.
Eat before you go to bed.

"Even though it's late now,
let's celebrate now.
You finally got your wish."
*Peter, Nathaniel, Zebedee's sons,
and Thomas learned how to fish.* (Repeat)

Jesus feeds us, Jesus leads us.
He is standing on our shore.
Come and eat and you'll be satisfied.
You will never ask for more.

Look for Jesus, listen close.
Then do what he tells you to.
Jesus is standing on your shore.
He is waiting there for you.

So if your net is empty
and you try to run the whole darn show,
Peter, Nathaniel, Zebedee's sons,
and Thomas say, "Let go!

"Drop your net down into the deep,
and you will always get your fill."
*Peter, Nathaniel, Zebedee's sons,
and Thomas know that you will.* (Repeat)

I'm Alive with Jesus

(See Romans 8:9-11)

Words and music by Julie Howard
Accompaniment by David Falzone

I'm a - live with Jesus, it's im -

pos - si - ble to hide.

Anawim Know

(See Luke 1:46-49, 51-53)

(Anawim: biblical term for the poor, the humble, the simple, God's little ones)

Words and music by Julie Howard
Accompaniment by David Falzone

1. My closets filled with fashion, I have all the latest styles. I seldom wear the same thing
2. My parents say they love me and they buy me lots of toys. I have my very own big
3. We just got back from Disneyland we're always on a plane. I've been in every state but
4. I'm in the highest reading group. I always get good grades. Each paper has a hap-py

1. twice.   But, inside I feel empty and I find it hard to smile. I
2. screen.   But, lately when I try to play I don't feel any joy. Please
3. two.   But, I am sick of airports and all beaches look the same I
4. face.   But, still I don't feel satisfied, I never have it made. I

watch it grow.

For the ending: Repeat and fade the last four measures of the chorus.

2. My
3. We
4. I'm

Gotta Do

(See Luke 6:41-42)

Words and music by Julie Howard
Accompaniment by David Falzone

When I point my fin-ger at you, three fin-gers point at me. [So you've got a lotta work to do be-fore you start to see. Be-

look in the mirror, do the old eye check.] Gotta see my - self like

oth - ers do, [gotta find that log and pull it through] be -

fore I point at you. Gotta do gotta do gotta

you, three fin - gers do not lie. [Now you

gotta see your own faults too, must look in your own

eye. God knows you, loves you, an - y - way, when you

41

next time you think I am wrong, just take some time to

sing this song.] Gotta see my-self like oth-ers do, [gotta

find that log and pull it through,] gotta say, "I make some

43

boo - boos too!" (Gotta do gotta do gotta do do do.) Gotta

do gotta do gotta do do do; be - fore I point at

you. Gotta do gotta do gotta do gotta do gotta

do gotta do gotta do. 〔Gotta do gotta do gotta

do gotta do gotta do gotta do gotta do.〕

We Goof But God Loves Us

(See Matthew 18:10-13)

Words and music by Julie Howard
Accompaniment by David Falzone

We messed up, we goofed up, we did it a-gain. We
messed up, we flubbed up, we blew it once more. We

let the dog out when he shoulda been in. Don't
spilled our spa-ghet-ti all o-ver the floor. We

yell and don't hol-ler, don't
make a big boo-boo most

scold and don't sue. We
ev-er-y day! We

goof but God loves us, will
goof but God loves us, Hoo-

you?

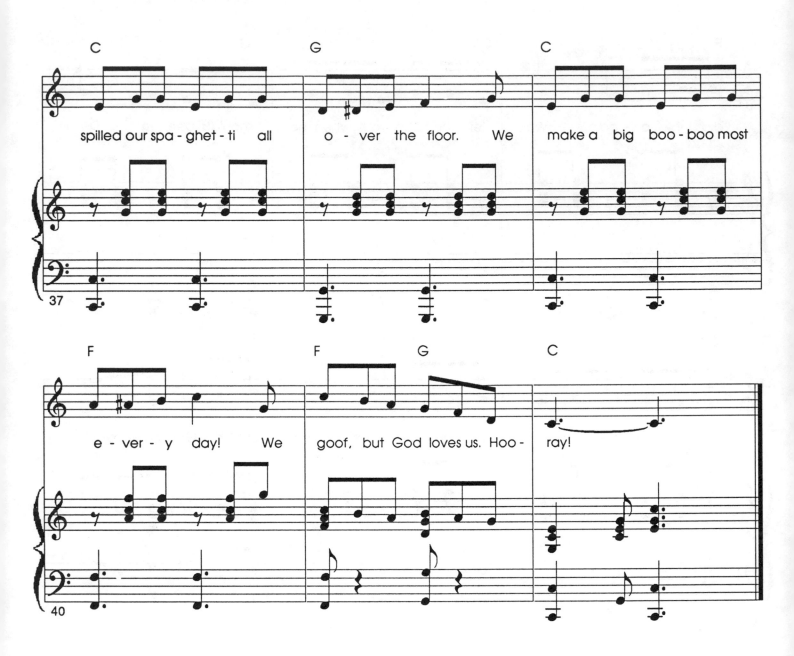

Don't Look for Jesus in the Sky

(See Acts 1:7-11)

Words and music by Julie Howard
Accompaniment by David Falzone

1. Don't look for Je - sus in the sky.
2. Don't look for Je - sus in the sky.

1. He's liv - ing down the block.
2. He's liv - ing right next door.

Bring him a piece of
Re - cog - nize him in

53

Knock

(See Luke 11:9-10)

Words and music by Julie Howard
Accompaniment by Jeff Velline and David Falzone

God Is Like the Dawn

(See John 8:12)

Words and music by Julie Howard
Accompaniment by David Falzone

1. Gently gives the world its sight, squeezing out the shadows of the
2. Seep in oh so gra - dual - ly, giving shape to sleeping bird and
3. Soft light from the sky a - bove, welcomed by the aspen and the

1. deep, dark, night. Fil - ling, flood - ing with her ho - ly light;
2. rust - ling tree. I see you and you..... see..... me;
3. mourn - ing dove. We can see now, we were made for love;

GOD IS LIKE THE DAWN!